Sammy
wins his way to fame

by Sonia Copeland Bloom

A red slug

With illustrations by Nick Page

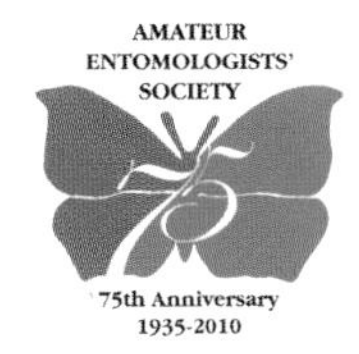

EDITORIAL FOREWORD

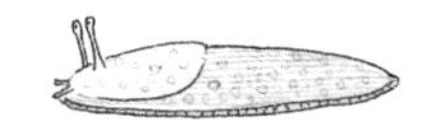

Slugs (and snails) are often given a very bad press. They are considered yucky, ugly and slimy, and lumped with all things horrid: "Slugs and snails and puppy dogs' tails, that is what little boys are made of." But actually, slugs are amazing and wonderful creatures if you only take the trouble to find out for yourself.

There are light grey ones, brown ones, dark grey ones, black ones, and even orange ones! Some even have a fancy orange trim or skirt. Are they slimy? Carefully and gently touch one (now wash your hands). No, they are not slimy. They do move around on a sticky slimy trail, but they are cool and dry to touch. Slugs are cool! Some slugs are so small you can hardly even see them ... some are so long they can almost stretch as long as your foot!

Slugs are more advanced than snails. They used to have a large cumbersome shell that stopped them from crawling into small cracks, crevices and cool places away from the sun which threatens to dry them out. Slugs lost most of their shells, but they still retain a remnant of the shell as a small plate or tiny calcareous granules in their tails. Without their shells, they can squeeze into cracks in the soil, slide under stones and bricks in the garden, and hide away from the sun. Slugs are clever and slugs are survivors. Just like Sammy.

So slugs are cool ... and Sonia Copeland Bloom tells us a story of a cool slug ... and gives us some more neat facts about slugs. Amaze your friends with what you know about slugs.

As an archaeological scientist, I have been looking at ancient microscopic shells since I was a student. I use the ancient shells to identify many different species which live in different habitats, so that I can interpret what the environment and land-use was like in the archaeological past, for example around Stonehenge. As a child I was fascinated by slugs and snails crawling along - all different shapes and sizes, some with big shells, some with tall shells and some with no shells at all. It is important that we appreciate the 100 plus species in Great Britain and ensure that there are a large variety of natural habitats where they can all survive.

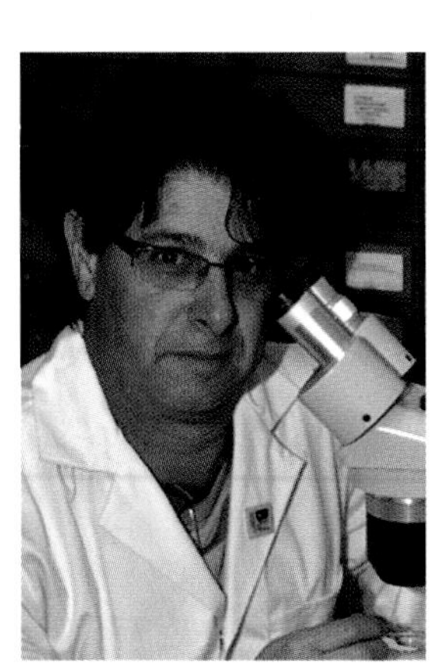

I hope that the story of Sammy the Slug will interest children and provoke them to look and explore for themselves, and care about their environment.

Dr Mike Allen, *President,*
Conchological Society of Great Britain & Ireland

The Conchological Society of Great Britain & Ireland (Founded 1876)

The Conchological Society of Great Britain and Ireland is one of the oldest existing societies devoted to the study of molluscs. We promote and support all forms of study and recording of molluscs (land and marine) in its widest aspects for the benefit of the public. We have a large membership with a wide and diverse range of interests. The Society is a Registered Charity and anyone, anywhere, may join. Our aims are achieved through meetings and workshops, publications (a journal and newsletter called *Mollusc World*), local and national recording schemes and grants.

Our members include young and old, professional and amateur all with a common interest. Come and join in. You can find more information at: **www.conchsoc.org**

The Amateur Entomologists' Society

Founded in 1935, the Amateur Entomologists' Society is a leading society for anyone interested in insects and their natural history. Its primary aim is to promote the study of entomology, especially amongst amateurs and young people, through the publication of books and periodicals and the organisation of educational events. There is also a popular Bug Club and *Bug Club Magazine* for younger members. If you would like to join, go to the Bug Club website below.

Visit our website: **www.amentsoc.org** and **www.amentsoc.org/bug-club**

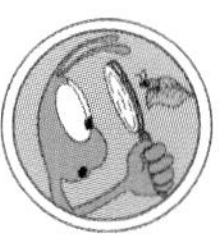

If you would like more information, write to:
The Amateur Entomologists' Society, PO Box 8774, London SW7 5ZG.

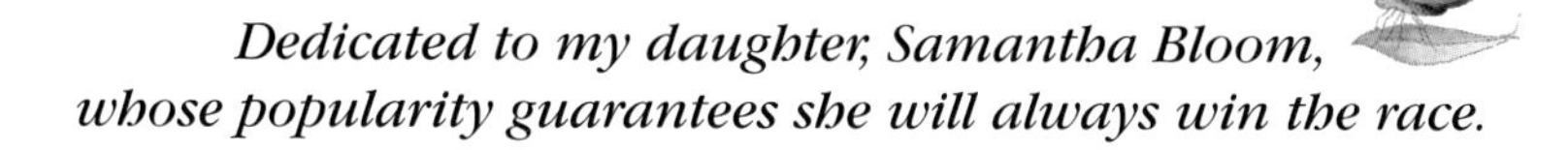

Dedicated to my daughter, Samantha Bloom,
whose popularity guarantees she will always win the race.

CONTENTS

Sammy the Slug
wins his way to fame

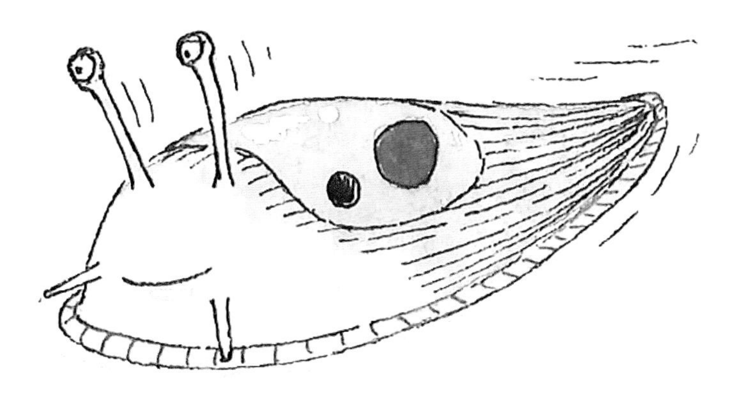

Slugs have an important role in the world and can be fascinating!

If you asked any of your friends whether or not they liked slugs - they may say, "Sorry! We're not too keen on slimy slugs!" Some people - but certainly not all - may even describe the slug as one of their least favourite creatures. Poor slugs! But believe it or not, slugs, which belong to a large group of animals known as **molluscs**, have an important place in the world. There are some fascinating facts about them and the good that they can do for us humans. Yes, believe me, the world would be a poorer place without the useful role they play in it.

The slime that slugs make is there for a good reason. It keeps them clean and protects them from their enemies as they crawl around the garden - leaving a sparkling, silvery trail. Like snails, they have four tentacles (or feelers): the long ones support their eyes, while the short ones help them smell and feel - helpful for navigating their crawl-abouts.

If you take a little time to study a slug, you will find it interesting. Slugs have a reputation for destroying many plants in our gardens. But they also munch up decaying vegetation, and thus have a useful role in tidying up gardens and the countryside.

Snails are almost identical to slugs, but their beautiful spiral shells have always made them more popular. Undoubtedly, snails devour our garden plants as much as slugs do - but slugs are more often blamed. However, slugs can move faster than snails and can stretch themselves out in a remarkable way. This makes them more adventurous, and worth backing if both are participating in slug and snail races!

One reason to like slugs is that they don't seem to object if you set them up for slug races, which can be a lot of fun, as long as you handle them gently and put them back in the garden afterwards.

Sammy is a large brown garden slug who lives in the Hornby family's garden at 6 Maple Way. He was sad and lonely because he felt nobody liked him. But Sammy found a friend one day and, after turning to him for advice, he won his way to fame and popularity.

This is his story.....

A Dusky slug in a garden

Rarely a day passed without Sammy complaining out loud that he wished and wished he had not been born a slug.

Woody the woodlouse had a good heart. "Sammy, you sound so miserable. What's wrong with being a slug?"

"Tell me something that's good about being a slug," moaned Sammy. "I'm slow and slimy brown. I take for ever to turn a corner. I find myself in trouble all the time for just – well, being me! Worst of all, nobody wants me as a friend!" At the end of Sammy's eye-tentacles, shining drops of self-pity glistened like diamonds.

Woody already knew that the **slime** on Sammy's coat was important, for it helped to protect him from being attacked by his enemies and kept his coat and the '**skirt**' that edged his body from being covered in dirt.

But after a quick glance at him, Woody realised that Sammy's slimy coat would not encourage a lot of his friends to give him a hug. Woody was proud of his grey, armour-like coat which he kept spotlessly clean and shiny.

Woody could see that Sammy was lonely. He knew how fortunate he was to come from a large family of woodlice who enjoyed a happy life in the rockery at the corner of the garden at 6 Maple Way, home of the Hornby family.

Sammy thought about his cousin Cedric Snail, who also lived in the garden and had a coiled shell on his back. "At least when snails are miserable they can curl up into their shells," he said enviously. "Everyone likes snails."

"My cousin, Cedric Snail, eats just as many plants as I do – but he rarely gets the blame. I do!"

Slugs, Woody agreed, were not popular with the other creatures in the garden. Slugs were blamed by everyone, even the Hornby family, for chewing more holes in lettuces, petunias and other plants than any other creature.

Woody looked at Sammy with sympathy in his kind eyes. "Don't despair," he said. "You can count me as your friend. So that's one friend you have already! Let's see what I can do!"

He went to visit Eddie the earthworm, busy as usual burrowing out a new tunnel.

"Eddie, could you be best friends, or even just friends with Sammy the slug?" he asked.

"Sorry, Woody," replied Eddie. "Slugs are not my favourite neighbours. Being so large, they usually take up all the best underground holes. We keep skidding on their slimy trails. It's best for me to avoid slugs. Look – there's a caterpillar over there. Ask her."

Woody went up to the yellow caterpillar who was crawling up a stalk.

"Hey, Caterpillar! Fancy being friends with a lonely slug?"

"Certainly not!" bristled the little caterpillar, wiggling the hairs on her humped back with irritation. She raised up her front half to speak sternly to Woody. "Listen Woody, I'm very busy with my **pupa** problems. I'm told it's time for me to turn into a **chrysalis**." Her mood changed as a faraway look came into her eyes. "Imagine! They say I'm going to turn into a stunning creature with wings when I wake up – blue as the sky with little white trims. I just can't wait – I'd better get weaving!"

So Woody hurried off, thinking it was a pity that there was no way Sammy could copy the caterpillar and transform himself into a beautiful creature.

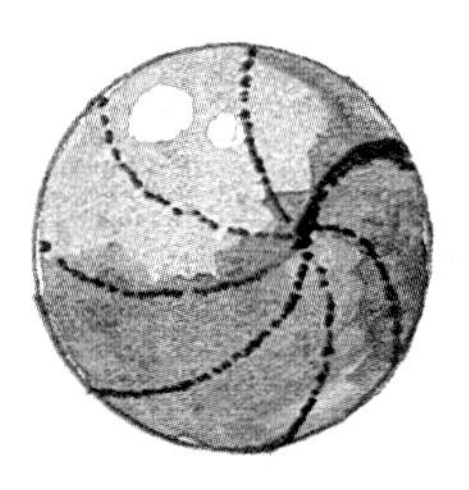

Woody curled into a ball to think about Sammy's problem.

What could the poor slug do to make himself more popular?

"He must stop grumbling for a start. It's not easy to help someone who moans all the time," he thought. "Everyone has bad times."

A Spanish slug exploring

It was the Easter holidays and the Hornby children – Thomas, his younger brother Hugo and their sister Little Lizzie – had decided to organise a slug and snail race in their garden and invite their friends to take part. While gathering food near the vegetable garden, Woody spotted Thomas sticking a notice on the water barrel. Thomas stepped back and read the words out loud.

The notice said:

Woody was listening. "That's cool!" thought Woody. "A slug and snail race would be just the thing to cheer Sammy up."

"Hello Woody!" A familiar voice called from the trees. It was Spinny the spider.

"Hi Spinny," said Woody. "I'm trying to cheer Sammy up. He thinks nobody likes him. I'm going to get him to go in for this slug and snail race. Sounds fun! If I can persuade him, Spinny, could you lend him some support – even if it's just to cheer him on?"

Spinny knew what a good friend Woody was to others. He was always there to help if he could.

"Of course I will, Woody. You hurry along to see if you can persuade him ... then leave the rest to me!"

On a nearby leaf, a fly had overheard the conversation between Woody and Spinny. It was Fly, well-known to all the creatures who lived in the Hornbys' garden. He was wary of Spinny, as he had often seen his friends caught up in one of Spinny's silky webs.

Fly chipped into the conversation, "So there's a kind streak in you somewhere is there, Spinny?" Spinny grinned mischievously. "You should know by now I've a warm heart, Fly. But we all have empty bellies to fill. Come nearer and I'll give you one of my sticky hugs!"

"No thanks," said Fly, knowing that Spinny's main diet was fly pie, and he flew off quickly. "I'll watch the race from a safe distance, thanks all the same!"

Woody hurried back to tell Sammy all about the Easter Race for slugs and snails.

"Come on, why don't you have a go?" he said. "Bet you slugs can move faster than snails. Even if you don't win, you may have some fun!"

Sammy looked doubtful. Then he saw Woody's face full of warmth and encouragement for him. He must stop being so dejected and gloomy, he told himself, even if only for Woody's sake.

So Sammy agreed to enter the race. He queued up under the damp plank by the line of carrots on the vegetable plot with some other snails and slugs, noticing with modest pride that he was one of the biggest. He saw that some snails were there too – and spotted Cedric Snail, his cousin. “Hope I will at least beat Cedric,” he thought.

A while later, the plank was lifted and Thomas Hornby crouched down and looked at all the slugs and snails lined up under it. “Come and look, we’ve got some beauties here!” he called to his younger brother Hugo. “Let’s pick the best slugs and snails to back for the race,” he said. “Lizzie, go and fetch a box that we can put them in.”

Hugo decided to choose Sammy and lifted up the slug with great care. Even so, Sammy shuddered when the saltiness of Hugo's hand stung him, as slugs can be harmed by salt. All the same, he felt proud that he had been picked. Hugo immediately remembered what his Dad had told him about picking up slugs, and he quickly placed Sammy on a leaf, while remembering he had to rinse his hands later. "That's better," said Sammy peering around him with both sets of tentacles.

Then he heard a small voice in the background which he recognised as Woody's. "C'mon Sammy – you can do it!" The slug felt excited by Woody's encouragement. Perhaps his luck would change!

A selection of garden slugs on the go!

Thomas returned with a shoe-box, which had holes in its lid, and placed all the slugs and snails inside, with some crisp lettuce leaves to keep them cool.

One of the slugs turned to Sammy and said coyly, "Hello, I'm Molly." Sammy nodded to her with his eye tentacles. Her friendliness made him feel better. He was glad now that Woody had made him go in for the race. The snails, including Cedric Snail, curled up quietly into their shells. Sammy thought that snails would find it more difficult to race with big shells on their backs and no longer envied them.

Just as the creatures were wondering what would happen next, the lid of the box opened and a number of faces peered down at them. As well as the Hornby children, their friends Peter and Holly, who lived next door, and Khali and Ashya, who lived opposite, had also come over to join in the fun.

Thomas pulled out a sheet of coloured circles from his pocket.

"We must stick a different coloured circle on each competitor," he said in his most organising voice, for both he and Hugo had put on garden slug and snail races before.

Sammy was pleased to hear Lizzie say, "The slug's slime is very useful, isn't it?"

"That's true," said Thomas. "And they say slugs can race faster than snails – they don't have a shell to drag along."

A Kentish snail

A Netted slug

"I prefer snails – so I shall back this big one," said Ashya, picking up Cedric, and sticking a yellow circle onto his shell. Sammy noticed Cedric Snail looking pleased at Ashya's compliment. He glanced at Sammy and gave him a rather smug smile.

Hugo lifted Sammy up onto a piece of lettuce leaf, holding him close to his face. "You are Red and belong to me," he said sticking a red circle on his back. "It feels good to be wanted," thought Sammy.

"And you are Green and belong to me," said Lizzie picking up Molly and balancing her on a piece of lettuce in the palm of her hand while she stuck a green circle on her back. Sammy and Molly waved tentacles at each other.

The other children picked out the remaining snails and slugs, sticking a different coloured circle on each of them. Everyone began to feel excited.

Thomas placed all the competitors in the middle of the round garden table underneath a tree. The children gathered around to watch.

Hugo had borrowed their mother's oven timer and now he wound it up ready to go. He then asked Khali to blow up a paper bag he had brought along, and to burst it with his hands when he gave the word so it would make a loud bang – imitating a starting-gun.

"First one to reach the edge of the table is the winner," announced Hugo. "All agreed?"

Everyone nodded.

"Ready, steady, GO!" shouted Hugo.

'BANG!' went the paper bag, frightening the birds in the nearby trees.

"Hurrah!" shouted all the children.

The slugs and snails waved their tentacles in the air. They slowly started moving in different directions.

Sammy lurched forward, not sure which direction to go. He heard a distant shout.

"Hey Sammy, can you spot me? I'm down here in the garden. Spinny the spider is in the tree watching you from above!"

Arion fasciatus slug

"It's Woody," Sammy thought, feeling happy to have a special friend who wanted him to win. Woody's support made him feel determined to do well.

"Come on Sammy!" Spinny called out from a tree near the table. "Move along as fast as you can. You can win this race. I know you can." Sammy waved a tentacle towards him in thanks.

"If I move over there, I may spot Woody down in the garden," he thought. Stretching his strong body out as hard and as far as he could, Sammy slid forward.

"I say!" said Peter. "Just look at Hugo's big slug, Red. He certainly knows where he's going." All the children were jumping up and down in excitement as if they were watching a mini Olympics.

Great Red slug

"Come on Blue – faster, faster!" shrieked Holly, whose red curls bobbed up and down as she watched her snail with a blue circle on its shell moving forward.

"Get a move on, Yellow, old fellow!" shouted Ashya to Cedric Snail, who was following Sammy, although not moving in such a streamlined way.

"Go on, go on Red, you old brick!" yelled Hugo to Sammy, who was definitely in front, stretching out even further now he knew that Hugo, Woody and Spinny all wanted him to win.

"Hurry up Green, you've got to be seen!" Little Lizzie called out, trying to encourage Molly. A note of despair had crept into her voice, for Molly seemed to be going around in circles.

"Wow! Just look at Red – he's a real mover. Go on Orange!" Thomas cried, envious of Red, as the snail he had picked with an orange circle had started to turn backwards.

Sammy swelled with pride. "My! I am popular today," he told himself.

"Come on Sammy, you're in front. Keep going!" called Spinny, waving from a web he had woven in the tree above the garden table especially so he could watch Sammy race. Fly swooped over the table. "Aren't I glad I've got wings – great for a quick getaway!" he whooped.

Sammy's strong muscles rippled as he slid along on his skirt, helped by its thick coating of slime. He soon came to the edge of the table. He peered down with his tentacles and there was Woody waving at him with a tiny white flag made from a daisy petal.

There was a loud ping as the oven timer went off to signal the end of the race.

"Two minutes and forty-eight seconds – brilliant! Red, the big slug, is the winner of the race and has broken all previous records," cried Hugo looking delighted. Thomas wrote out the score with a stub of chalk on a toy blackboard.

Everyone burst out cheering. Sammy, placed on a lettuce leaf, was lifted up in triumph by Hugo who announced, "Red is the Champion and deserves a gold medal as the winner. I hereby name him the best slug in the garden!" Sammy felt so proud he couldn't stop waving all four tentacles around in happiness.

Cedric Snail had been overtaken by two slugs so was not even a bronze winner but, nevertheless, he sportingly went up to Sammy to

congratulate him for winning. “You’re lucky not having a shell when it comes to racing or playing hide and seek,” said Cedric.

“Wow!” cried Sammy, trying to take in his sudden fame and popularity. “I’m going to have to get used to this.” He no longer felt either miserable or unloved. In fact, he felt as if he were glowing all over with delight.

Later that afternoon, when Thomas and Hugo had put the slug and snail competitors carefully back into the garden, a crowd of the local creatures gathered to congratulate Sammy, the champion slug of No. 6 Maple Way, for being the winner of the race. Everyone voted to hold a party to celebrate Sammy’s success.

Molly had come last in the race, declaring she had got lost half-way through. But she was very pleased that Sammy had won. She gave him a slug-hug and whispered in his ear, “Well done, Hero! Will you take me back home after the party so I don’t get lost again?”

Sammy nodded happily, thinking how pretty Molly looked.

Woody and Spinny exchanged winks.

“Sammy’s become the most popular slug in the garden,” said Spinny. “And now he has a real best friend – thanks to you Woody!”

“Not really,” replied Woody. “I just lent a hand – and told him to stop moaning. He did the rest himself.”

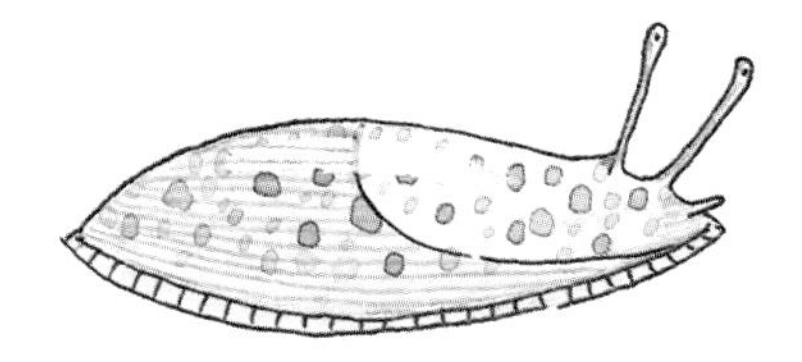

THE HORNBY FAMILY AND THEIR GARDEN

In the suburb of a town, perhaps not far from where you live, is a pleasant house and garden at No. 6 Maple Way, home of the Hornby family, Mr and Mrs Hornby and their three children, Thomas, nearly eight, Hugo, nearly seven and Little Lizzie, now four. It is their beautiful garden that is the setting for all the stories in the Tales & Truths about Garden Minibeasts series.

Mr and Mrs Hornby are keen gardeners, like many people are the world over, and want their children to grow up respecting and showing consideration to all wildlife. They want them to understand the huge importance of the natural world to our future. The children have been astonished to learn that without the hard work of tiny insects and other invertebrates, which includes the essential work of worms who till the soil for every kind of root to grow, the world's eco-system that provides life on earth could not exist.

The children haven't needed much persuading to be fascinated by the insects and other tiny creatures they could find in their garden. They keep some of them as pets in the house for a short while, to learn more about them.

There is a special area at the bottom of the Hornbys' garden which they leave untended, full of wildflowers and a variety of grasses, an old log and a gnarled old apple tree. A small pond provides essential water for all wildlife; this especially attracts dragonflies, damselflies, pond skaters and water beetles. In the pond, the children can find **larvae** of many other insects, and, in the spring, frogspawn. When the spawn hatches, the children keep a few of the tadpoles in a jam-jar to watch them grow into frogs.

As well as enjoying their garden in many different ways throughout the year, the Hornbys look for ways to make the garden attractive to useful insects, such as ladybirds, ground beetles, and bees. For example, they plant flowers that attract such insects, including primroses, buddleia, lavender, heather, mallow, golden rod, honeysuckle, sunflowers and night-scented stock. Some of these plants are very sweetly scented and they strongly attract nectar-seeking insects, particularly beautiful butterflies.

They also create a range of different **habitats** for wildlife. A rockery in a sunny spot, covered with colourful rockery plants, provides a refuge for woodlice and other invertebrates, as well as being a place for butterflies to sun themselves on. Most useful of all is a log-pile placed in a damp, shady spot, made with bark-covered hardwood logs. This can soon become a flourishing wildlife community for beetles, woodlice, spiders, millipedes and centipedes as well as slugs and snails.

Mr Hornby built a simple compost bin so the family can now reduce the amount of their waste by putting suitable, organic leftover remains in it. Mrs Hornby also insisted on a wormery box by the backdoor, not only because she knows worm manure helps keep diseases and pests at bay, but so that the whole family could watch worms at work, turning the waste into rich and valuable compost. Worm manure not only improves the soil, it increases the level of moisture retention in soil, thus helping plants to grow with less water. They all agreed that ploughing worm manure back into their garden increases its yield, particularly producing large, tastier fruits and vegetables.

The Hornbys never use insecticides as they know these do more harm than good in a garden. Most pesticides can contaminate and fatally harm minibeasts and small animals that become food for other creatures, such as birds, worms, frogs and hedgehogs, just to name a few.

Thomas has a pet slug – a large grey one he found on the garden path, and Hugo keeps a small collection of both slugs and snails. They observe them mate, lay eggs and are writing a diary about them for a school project. They know slugs and snails can devour some of the plants and vegetables they grow. They make sure they only use a range of humane deterrents (see page 35) which they place around plants to stop them from doing too much harm. Mr Hornby reminds the children that slugs have a useful role by eating dead leaves and other garden debris. And, as part of the **food-chain**, they provide protein-rich food for other creatures.

As well as slug and snail races, the children and their friends organise scent trails, treasure hunts, competitions to find the most number of unusual leaves, and have even made garden scrapbooks. Gardens can be wonderful places to explore and learn from, but equally, so can local parks and the countryside. If you don't have a garden, there are many other things you can do to spend time outdoors, and you could also grow flowers and herbs in pots or window-boxes.

ACTIVITY: Make a list of all the ways you could make a garden attractive to insects and other small creatures as the Hornby family do. There are many ideas you can find on BBC Gardening Sites for children, or by exploring the Amateur Entomologists' Society website: **www.amentsoc.org/gardening-for-insects** where there are also links to more advice on wildlife gardens. Family bug-hunts are great fun so visit **www.amentsoc.org/bug-club** to join in, or best of all, join the Bug Club where you will learn more about insects, attend visits to museums and meet other children with similar interests. The Conchological Society also run interesting events so try them on **www.conchsoc.org** and become an expert on slugs and snails.

Keeping Slugs as Pets

Making a slugarium

Northern Field slug

SLUGS make wonderful pets. You can find them in your garden during early mornings or late at night, especially after rain, leaving a silvery trail behind them. Why not keep one or two as pets? It's not difficult to make a **Slugarium** but before you do, you must make sure you have the time to feed your new pets and keep the habitat or garden you have made for them clean and fresh.

Find a couple of the largest and healthiest-looking slugs you can. Then find a large escape-proof Perspex container or box. To keep slugs as pets, in order to study them, a small aquarium would make an ideal home as long as it has a proper lid. Make sure it is not kept in direct sunlight as slugs prefer dark, damp conditions to live in. Remember, slugs can disappear through the tiniest of cracks by stretching themselves out to be long and thin. They are strong and muscular, covered with slime, which allows them to move over almost any surface.

Put a layer of fine gravel at the bottom of the tank for drainage. Then add a few inches of lump-free earth from the garden. The soil needs to be kept moist and the container humid by having a shallow dish (such as a jam-jar lid) containing water, with a piece of kitchen towel in it. You should also buy a sprayer so you can spray the sides of the slugs' home to keep the atmosphere moist for them. Covering the soil with moss also helps to keep the moisture in. Then decorate the Slugarium as if you were making a miniature garden with pieces of bark, and leaves. Put a few plant leaves in it for slug food. Slugs eat a huge variety of leaves, including dead leaves. They especially like dandelions and nettles. They'll eat vegetables and fruit, so put in food scraps such as cucumber, kale and pieces of apple or tops of strawberries. Don't forget to give your slugs (or slug) a name.

Chestnut slug

You should carefully wash your hands before touching your slug, as humans have salty hands and salt hurts slugs. Also, you should wash the slime off your hands afterwards. If you want to learn more about keeping slugs as pets, contact the Conchological Society (details listed on inside of front cover). It would be a good idea to write a diary about your experiences of keeping a slug as a pet - this, together with your slug, could be a valuable contribution to your school's nature table. And, if you go away on holiday, your slug won't mind at all if you tip it back into the garden - in a cool, dark place.

The Slug in my Garden

Dear Slug, how slowly you move.
You can see the shimmering slime twinkling in the moonlight.
Your shining trail, always so bright.
You hide away when you see the sunlight,
But come out when it's the sun's turn to hide at night.
You may be different from others though,
That's why I love you so!

Poem by **Samantha Rogers, aged 10**
Langham C.E. Primary School, Rutland

First prize competition winner in the Tales & Truths 'There's a Slug in my Garden' *poetry competition, judged by the President of the The Conchological Society of Great Britain and Ireland, Dr Mike Allen.*

Drawing by **Charlotte Price, aged 9**
Langham C.E. Primary School, Rutland

Fascinating Facts about Slugs

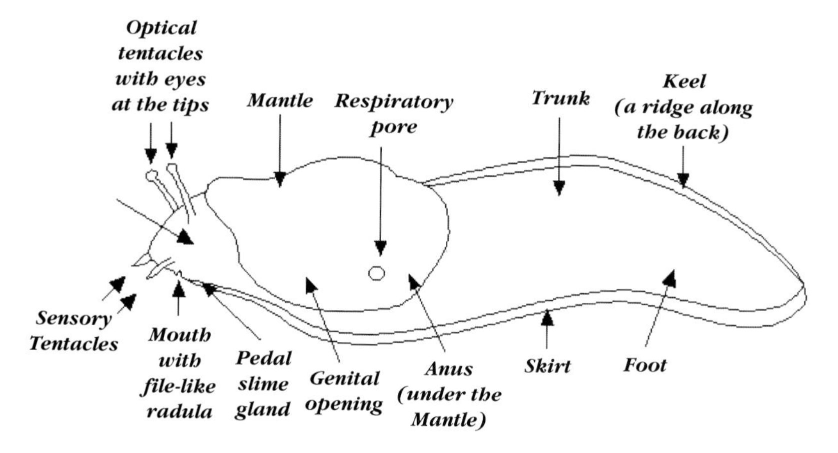

Slugs are most closely related to snails, part of the large group known as molluscs. **Molluscs** were among the first inhabitants of the Earth. We know this because **fossils**, found by scientists, date them back to some 600 million years. That is a great deal longer than human beings.

There are many slugs and snails that live on the land. But there are many other kinds of mollusc, that live in the sea or other water and all have soft bodies and no segments. It is believed that there are between 60,000 and 80,000 species of slugs and snails in the world, and about 120 different **species** in Great Britain! In spite of being rather unpopular because of their slimy appearance and their habit of eating garden plants, there are some very interesting facts about slugs.

Molluscs, the large group of **invertebrates** that includes slugs, are scientifically known as the **phylum Mollusca**. This name describes their soft, fleshy bodies.The Mollusca are divided into a number of groups called **Classes**.The slugs and snails belong to the second largest class in the animal kingdom called **Gastropoda** or **gastropods**, which means 'stomach foot' and describes the muscular foot on which they travel.The gastropods are divided into a number of **Orders**. One of these orders includes the snails and slugs that live on land. These breathe air with a lung and they have two pairs of tentacles. Other members of the mollusc phylum include: octopuses, oysters, clams, limpets and squids.

A Tiger slug

By expanding and contracting the strong muscles of its one foot, which is surrounded by a foot fringe called a skirt, a slug can move along at about 2.5 to 5 cm (1 or 2 inches) a minute. Although many species are brown or grey because these are good camouflage colours, others are white, yellow or purple. Some have patterns, such as the common Leopard slug, which is grey with black spots and known for being a predator of other slugs.

The common grey field slug is among the commonest of British species. Unfortunately slugs are unpopular with gardeners and farmers for a good reason - they eat plants and valuable crops. However, the slug still has a valuable role to play in the world. Many small animals, such as birds, moles, ducks and some types of beetle are partial to eating the protein-filled slug so, as mentioned before, slugs have an important role to play in the food chain. Slugs also help make our soil more fertile by eating up dead leaves and garden debris. This helps plants and crops to grow more successfully.

SLIME: If you stroke a slug along its **keel** (which usually looks like a thin dark line along its back), the slime that covers it will feel slippery. The slime comes off on your fingers but you can wipe it off with a leaf. The slime makes sure that the slug keeps clean. Watch your slug moving in the garden and you can see for yourself that any dirt he picks up will slip off, because of the slime. The interesting fact about a slug's slime is that it's a natural **anaesthetic**. It does the same job as the dentist does when he numbs your teeth before drilling them! If you were to lick a slug - definitely not recommended though - your tongue would become numb.

Slugs have four tentacles (feelers) that look like little horns sticking up from the tops of their heads. The longer pair of tentacles, known as **optical tentacles**, have little black dots at the ends of them, which are the slug's eyes. Slugs don't see very well. The smaller pair work as the slug's nose. They can detect odours or chemicals in the air. If you touch a tentacle, it will immediately draw back temporarily.

To find food, slugs poke about with their tentacles, which they can also pull in under their mantle (see the diagram on page 32). This covers them like a little cloak behind their optical tentacles.

Slugs are **hermaphrodites**. If you say it out loud slowly - herm-aphrodite - it's easier to pronounce.This means they have both male and female **reproductive systems** inside them to make baby slugs, but they usually need other slugs in order to have babies. The parts of the slug which they use for having babies is called **genitalia** (see Genital opening on the diagram on page 32). These are covered by the mantle.

Slugs lay thousands of eggs in places that always remain damp like rotting wood or under rocks. The eggs are tiny - yellow or greenish white balls. Young slugs look like their parents, except, of course, they are much smaller.

Dusky slugs mating

As we have explained above, the slug's one foot has very strong muscles, which it ripples in order to slide along. If you place a slug on a piece of clear plastic and watch it from underneath, you will be able to see its amazing rippling muscles as it moves. Land-dwelling slugs eat various leafy plants, being particularly fond of nettles, dandelions and, unfortunately, many other plants you may have in your garden. However, it's worth noting that there are a number of plants they do not devour.

There are a few kinds of slug, including the Leopard slug - mentioned above - that will eat other invertebrates, including other slugs. The slug's mouth can be found underneath its body, so it has to crawl over its food to eat. If you look at the slug's underside through clear plastic, as suggested above, you can see the slug's rasping, sharp tongue, called a **radula**. This is rather like a ribbon, full of up to an amazing 27,000 teeth, which the slug uses to scrape up food to put into its mouth.

YOUR COUNTY WILDLIFE TRUST

There are 47 county Wildlife Trusts in Britain, often with their own nature reserves and events.

Wildlife Trusts, The Kiln, Waterside, Mather Road,
Newark, Notts. NG24 1WT. Tel 01636 677711
Email: enquiry@wildlifetrusts.org Website: www.wildlifetrusts.org

Humane Ways to Protect your Garden from Slugs

Slugs, as you may now agree, are fascinating creatures. Sadly, yes, they do enjoy eating the plants in our gardens, which makes them unpopular, but there are a number of humane ways of deterring slugs. It is every gardener's responsibility to use environmentally-friendly organic methods to control slugs and snails, while at the same time helping to improve the soil. These unpopular molluscs, it should be remembered, also eat up garden debris and help to make your garden soil more fertile too.

It's a great idea for children to be allowed to have their own patch of garden to grow things in and to be responsible for. A wise strategy is to choose plants, including vegetables, that are particularly resistant to slugs because they are not so high on the mollusc menu. Many such plants are available for the flowerbed, including: acanthus, agapanthus, anemones, antirrhinums, asters, cornflowers, fuchsias, geraniums, nasturtiums, peonies, pinks, tulips and wallflowers - all particularly effective if grown among others that you would wish to protect.

There are many humane ways of deterring slugs, which will interest children. For example, they can help to protect plants by surrounding them with things such as: used coffee grounds, grit or gravel, soot, ashes, crushed egg-shells or nuts, pine needles or cut hair collected from hairdressers and copper tape placed around a raised bed or pot is very effective. Best of all, seaweed collected on trips to the beach is a natural repellent, as slugs hate salt. Many of these ways of protecting your plants will also enrich your soil with calcium and other valuable minerals.

Probably the very best way to control the slugs in your garden (and by far

Spanish slug

Netted slug

my favourite way) is to go out when it's dark, particularly when it's been raining, carrying a torch. Collect every slug (and snail) you can see, not forgetting the light-coloured babies. Put them in an escape-proof plastic box and, the next day, take them to the nearest area away from people's gardens or food crops (e.g. woodland open to the public), where they can make new homes for themselves. If you do this several times, you will find that your slug population will decrease dramatically.

As a message for children - don't forget to spread the word. Every living animal plays its part in helping other kinds of creatures to survive - and that includes slugs. Avoid some of the unnecessary cruel ways suggested or advertised on-line for disposing of slugs. We all need trees, plants and grassy fields for raising animals and to use for growing food crops. Take time to marvel about the many different ways in which even common garden creatures, including the tireless earthworms, who aerate the soil around plant roots, can help us survive in almost every sort of landscape, in hot or cold climates and in varying weather conditions. The network of all life on earth, including human-beings is called the **ecosystem**.

Set an example to your friends by letting them see how important it is to treasure all those creatures you can find in your garden, because, together, they help to meet the daily needs of humans, like you and me. Remember that slugs have an important role in the world too, so need your consideration. And, by the way, that slug you might have stepped on - could be Sammy!

Durham slug eggs

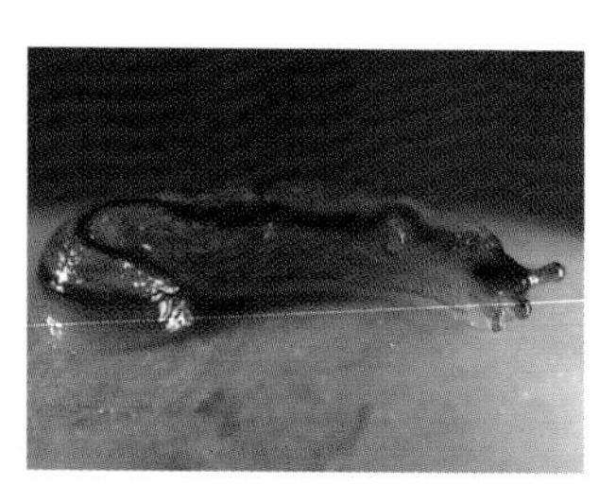

Juvenile Durham slug

To learn more about slugs, snails and molluscs, recommended books include:

- Janus, H. 1979. *The young specialist looks at land and freshwater molluscs.* London: Burke Books
- Beedham, G.E. 1972. *Identification of the British Mollusca.* Amersham: Hulton Educational Publications Ltd
- Kerney M.P. and Cameron, R.A.D. 1979. *A Field Guide to the Land Snails of Britain and North-west Europe.* London: Collins
- Kerney, M.P. 1999. *Atlas of the land and freshwater molluscs of Britain and Ireland.* Colchester: Harley Books

GLOSSARY

Includes all words highlighted in bold in the book

Anaesthetic: A medical/artificial method of taking away pain - e.g. often used by dentists!

Camouflage: Various methods of concealment that allows otherwise visible animals or objects to remain unnoticed or blend with their environment by resembling something else.

Chrysalis: See pupa.

Class: One of the groupings used to classify living things (e.g. see Gastropoda, below).

Ecosystem: The plants and animals that are found in a particular location are referred to as an ecosystem. These plants and animals depend on each other to survive.

Food Chain: This describes how a series (or a "chain") of living things feed on other living things in order get the energy they need. For most living things, their energy comes originally from sunlight. A food chain begins when a plant gathers energy from sunlight, using water and nutrients dissolved in the water. The chain continues when an animal (for example an insect) feeds on the plant. Then another animal eats the insect, and so-on and so-on! Children get energy from the food they eat each day.

Fossils: Objects preserved in strata of rock and recognisable as remains or vestiges of plants or animals of the past, usually prehistoric, ages. e.g. fossil bones or shells.

Gastropoda or gastropods: The class of molluscs that includes slugs and snails. The name means "stomach foot," since these animals crawl on the undersides of their bodies.

Copse snail

Genitalia: The parts of the body used for mating and producing eggs or babies.

Habitat: An area with the particular environmental conditions that an animal needs to live.

Hermaphrodite: An animal which has both male and female reproductive systems.

Invertebrate: An animal without a backbone. Invertebrates make up 95% of all creatures on earth.

Keel: The name of the thin dark line along a slug's back.

Larva (pl. Larvae): The juvenile form of an insect such as a ladybird beetle, which looks very different from the adult.

Molluscs: A large group (phylum) of invertebrates (animals without backbones), which includes slugs, snails, octopuses and squids.

Navigate: To find one's way somewhere and keep one's course.

Orders: One of the groupings used to classify living things: e.g. the Class Insecta (insects) can be divided into a number of Orders.

GLOSSARY (continued)

Phylum Mollusca: See Molluscs.

Pollinate or pollination: The process by which pollen is transferred from one plant to another.This can be by wind, or by being carried by insects who visit the flowers for nectar.

Proteins: A group of complex substances found in all living things and essential in the diet of many of them, including all animals.

Pupa: The sleeping stage of an insect, which eventually moults and becomes the adult stage (as in a butterfly, often called a chrysalis).

Radula: The slug's sharp tongue, full of miniature teeth which the slug uses to scrape up food to eat.

Reproductive system: The anatomical structures associated with reproduction - the process by which cells and organisms produce other cells and organisms of the same kind. The reproduction of organisms by the union of male and female reproductive cells (gametes) is called sexual reproduction.

Skirt: A fringe around the foot of a slug containing muscles which help the slug move along.

Slime: A rather off-putting (to humans) sticky substance found, for example, on slugs, snails, frogs or oozy mud.

Slugarium: A suitable homemade box or aquarium especially adapted to house slugs.

Species: A species is a group of organisms that can breed and produce fertile offspring.The name of each species is always written as the name of the genus it belongs to (with the first letter in capitals) followed by its own specific name (beginning with a lower case letter).

Spirally coiled shell: Shell on a snail which is wound into a coil or sometimes a cone.

Tentacles (or feelers) or Optical tentacles: The long, slender flexible appendage of an animal, used for feeling, grasping or moving, as in the snail. Optical tentacles support a slug's or snail's eyes.

White-lipped Banded snail

For further information on these words, and to look up hundreds of other entomology terms, you can check out the AES online glossary: www.amentsoc.org/insects/glossary

To research further information about Slugs and Snails and special words for Mollusc's go to www.conchsoc.org

Author's Last Word

One of the greatest rewards and privileges I have had as a result of researching and writing about garden minibeasts and small animals for the *Tales & Truths about Garden Minibeasts* series over the last few years, has been discovering so much about the lives of these small creatures who usually live their extraordinary lives just a stone's throw away from us. By sharing in their lives, by keeping them as pets to observe and understand, I have learned to love and appreciate them, and to care for them - not only for their extraordinary beauty, colours, intelligence and survival skills - but also for the work they do, tirelessly, to enhance my life - and yours.

Moving on to the subject of this book, molluscs or slugs to be exact, I quickly learned with some research and observation, how fascinating slugs can be. Like Sammy, they can't help being born a slug and we gardeners must have a responsibility to find humane ways to protect the plants we don't want the slugs in our gardens to eat, or how else will slugs know they are out-of-bounds? But during my research, which moved me so deeply, I was appalled by what I believe to be incredibly cruel and inhumane ways that modern man has invented for destroying garden slugs. Even responsible gardeners who dole out advice on popular websites or in books on gardening sold in reputable bookshops, provide a list of grisly tortures to inflict on these poor hapless creatures which are far too horrendous to print on these pages. I hope those reading this far, will rather turn to *Humane Ways to Protect Your Garden from Slugs* on page 35 where far more effective and humane ways to deal with the universal slug problem are listed. Also I hope that if families read this book together and keep a slug as a pet, maybe it could be an opportunity to help mitigate the terrible press that the poor slug seems to attract.

There are many invertebrate study societies and small clubs in most countries throughout the world, whose members passionately dedicate themselves to researching every possible type of invertebrate: be they our friends - or our foes. Surely the time has come for many more people, especially families and their children, to join such societies in their valuable work of promulgating the importance of invertebrates to humans, particularly critical today, for all the problems that face our world and its future.*

The Amateur Entomologists' Society (AES) endorsed the first books, as they have this one, the fifth in the series of six, because they hope, as I do, that the books' "audacious new approach to engaging children with the natural world" will also spark a new interest in natural history amongst the very young.

Governments are realising, and even passing edicts, about the importance of providing a gateway to the study and appreciation of wildlife among young people who, of course, will ultimately be responsible for the future of our world.

**See* Natural Childhood, *commissioned by the National Trust, written by Stephen Moss, about nature-deficit children and the dire effects that lack of contact with nature is having on our children today - visit www.scribd.com/doc/87203073*

The Slug in my Garden

There's a slug in my garden
I saw it in the night,
Glittering in the moonlight
Its protective coat
Looks like a shimmering boat
Gliding along in the darkness blue.

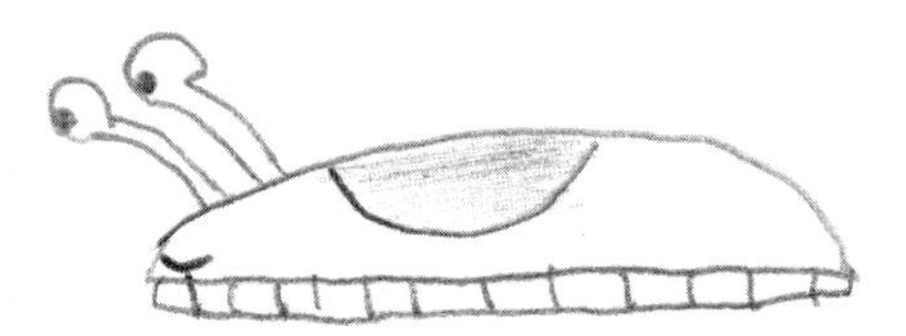

Poem by **Georgie Lamb, aged 9**
Langham C.E. Primary School, Rutland

Second prize-winner in the Tales & Truths 'There's a Slug in my Garden' *poetry competition, judged by the President of the The Conchological Society of Great Britain and Ireland, Dr Mike Allen.*

Drawing by **Daniel Bland, aged 10**
Langham C.E. Primary School, Rutland

Acknowledgements

I would like to thank the Conchological Society of Great Britain and Ireland, who kindly agreed to co-publish this book with the Amateur Entomologists' Society. I am grateful to their Officers who have generously given us their time, particularly the current President, Dr Mike Allen and former President Bas Payne, now Hon. Programme Secretary. Also to Hon. General Secretary, Rosemary Hill; Hon. Treasurer, Nick Light; Hon. Editor of the Society Journal, Dr Roy Anderson; Hon. Editor of *Mollusc World*, Peter Topley; Hon. Non-Marine Recorder, Adrian Norris; Hon. Conservation Officer, Dr Martin Willing; Hon. Webmaster, Dr Steve Wilkinson and to all the Council members. Also special thanks to our photographers, member Brian Eversham and Peter Topley, Editor of *Mollusc World*, who kindly supplied us with their stunning photographs of slugs.

Both The Conchological Society and I would also like to thank the AES's Council of Trustees, and the Publications Committee, especially Dr David Lonsdale, Dr Kieren Pitts, Jacqueline Ruffle and Hon. Secretary, Dafydd Lewis for their assistance in all aspects of the *Tales & Truths* production. Nick Page is to be applauded for his popular illustrations and hard work in ensuring anatomical correctness. I would particularly like to thank most warmly Carole Fries, whose professional skills in editing are, as always, invaluable to me.

There was a very high standard of entries and interest in our poetry competition "There's a Slug in my Garden" set for Class 5 of Langham C.E.Primary School, Rutland. Judged by the President of the Conchological Society, Michael Allen, winners were: 1st, Samantha Rogers, 2nd, Georgie Lamb and 3rd, Maddie Stellmacher. Runners-up were: Joshua Bland, Lizzie Beach, Jenna Burberry, Harry Mathers, Tegan Mould, Harry Peacock, Rose Wharton and Charlotte Wills. Congratulations to all and to Mrs. Suzanne Coughlan, Deputy Headteacher for helping us to organise it.

A special thank-you to my marvellous family for their encouragement, including Samantha, my daughter (to whom this book is dedicated); to Orlando, my son and Miranda, my daughter-in-law and to Flynn, my grandson – the best present life has ever given me. Finally, I would also like to thank another inspirational person who has given me valuable encouragement, Therese Kerr (www.theresekerr.com) and last, but not least, my partner Charles Lord.